Name: _____

Form: _____

Variation & Classification

- Read, engage and learn!

- Read the full colour, illustrated Topic Booklet.

- Use the Active Learning Game and Flashcards.

- Complete this Write Your Own Notes Booklet.

This Oaka™ Books Write Your Own Notes Booklet goes hand in hand with the Active Learning Pack on this topic. The pack includes a Topic Booklet, an Active Learning Game and Question & Answer Flashcards.

Fresh Focus on Learning

Variation & Classification Glossary

Abdomen: ....
....
....
....

Has gills?
No   Yes

Classification Key: ....
....
....
....

Amphibian: ....
....
....
....

Discontinuous: ....
....
....
....

Animal: ....
....
....
....

Environment: ....
....
....
....

Characteristics: ....
....
....
....

Genes: ....
....
....
....

Classification: ....
....
....
....

Group: ....
....
....
....

Cold Blooded: ....
....
....
....

Identification: ....
....
....
....

Continuous: ....
....
....
....

Inherited: ....
....
....
....

Correlation: ....
....
....
....

Insect: ....
....
....
....

Interpret: ....

Reptile: ....

Invertebrate: ....

Species: ....

Kingdom: ....

Specimen: ....

Mammal: ....

Subdivide: ....

Offspring: ....

Mammals
Fish
Amphibians
Reptiles
Birds
Taxonomy: ....

Observe: ....

Variation: ....

Organism: ....

Vertebrate: ....

Plant: ....

Warm Blooded: ....

1 — Species and Variation

- Living things of the same type belong to the same ....

- **Variation** means .... within a ....

- A dog is one **species**, but there are many different .... of dog.

- Dalmation, ... and Labrador are all one **species**, but there is a lot of .... between them.

2 — Variation

- What **variation** is there in these domestic cats?

- Eye ...., ..., colour and length of ...... are all **variations**.

3 — Human Variation

- Humans are a ...., but there is a lot of .... within our **species**.

- .... and .... colour, height, arm span and .... are all **variations**.

4 What is a Species?

- **Species** often have very different .... **But** some .... are very similar, like horses and donkeys.

- It gets confusing, so we need a definition.

The definition we use is:

- A .... is a group of .... that can breed together and have .... The **offspring** can also ....

- Horses and donkeys are .... species. They can breed together, but their offspring (a mule) **cannot** .... So, mules are not a ....

5 Characteristics

- Many .... are passed down from generation to generation.

- These **characteristics** are ....

- .... colour, eye colour and .... colour are all .... from our .... parents.

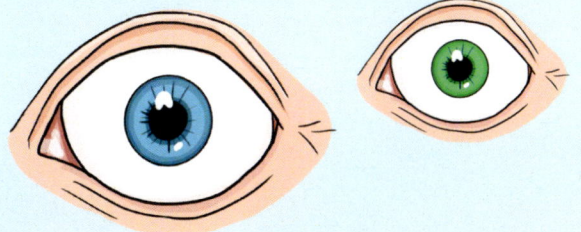

6 Inheriting Variation

But...

- We are not identical to either parent. We show ....

7   Passing on Characteristics

- We .... half of our .... **makeup** from our .... and half from our ....

- These **inherited** .... are called .... **variations**.

8   Control of Characteristics

- Your .... colour and some .... are caused by **inherited** .... information.

9   Male or Female?

- Your .... is **inherited** ....

10   Inherited and Environmental

- **Variation** can be caused by **both** .... and .... **factors**.

- Twins who grow up in .... places may show a lot of ....

11   Environmental Factors

- ...., ... and culture are all .... **factors**.

- Environmental factors cause .... **variation** in a species.

12   Environment and Variation

- Your hair may get .... in the sun, and your .... may get darker (sun tan).

- Your **skin colour (tan)**, ..., **religion and the** .... you speak, are all **environmental** ....

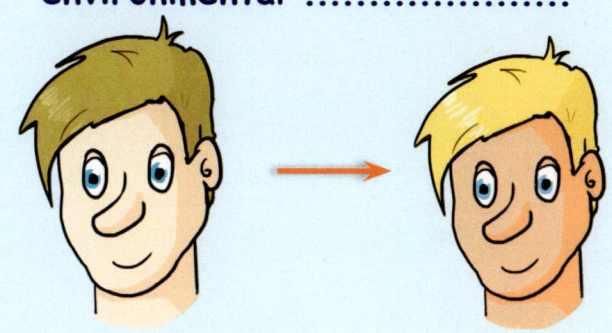

13   Environmental Factors and Plants

- **Environmental factors** cause variation in .... too.

- One .... of plant will have blue or pink flowers depending on the .... it is in.

Alkali
(P.H. above 7)

Acid
(P.H. below 7)

14   A Bit of Both

- Take two cuttings from the **same** plant.

- Grow one in .... soil and the other in .... soil.

- The plants will grow ....

Good Soil   Bad Soil

15 Discontinuous Variation

- .... is where characteristics can .... fall into certain groups.

- You can .... be male or female.

- Your blood group can .... be AB, A, B or O.

16 Tally Chart

- We can use a .... to collect information (data) for .... **variation**.

- We can then plot a .... from the data.

Blood Group	Number of People
A	IIII IIII IIII
B	IIII IIII I
AB	IIII IIII IIII IIII
O	IIII IIII IIII II

17 D.................. Variation

- We must use a .... to present our data.

- A bar chart is used to plot .... answers.

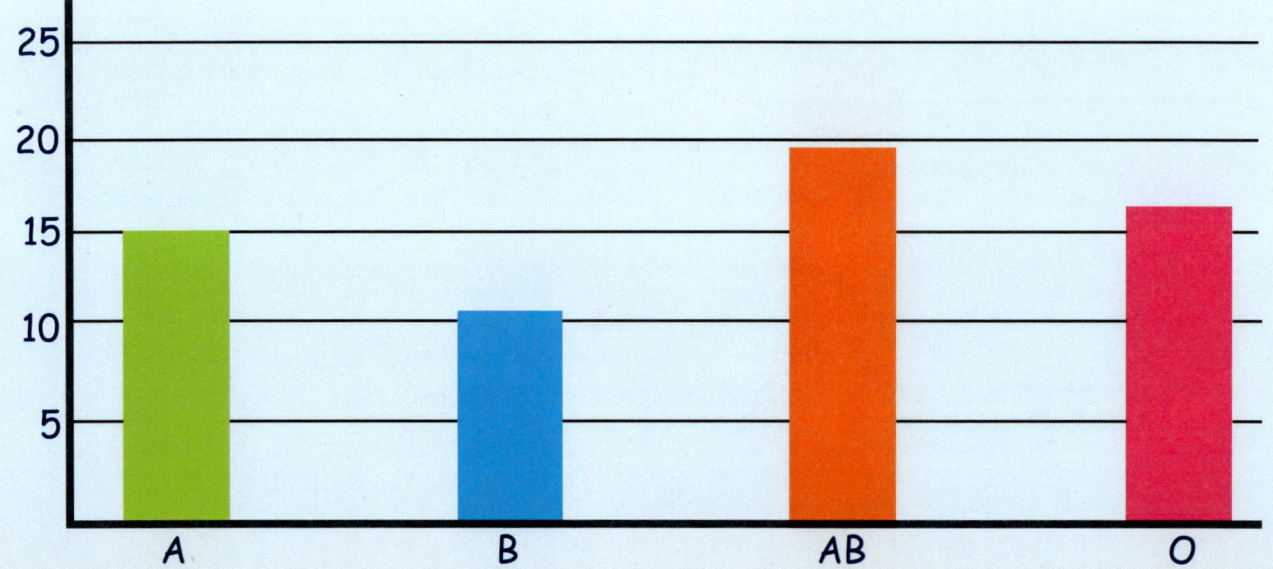

18 .... Variation

- When characteristics can fall .... **along a** .... they show **continuous** ....

- For example ...., ... or weight.

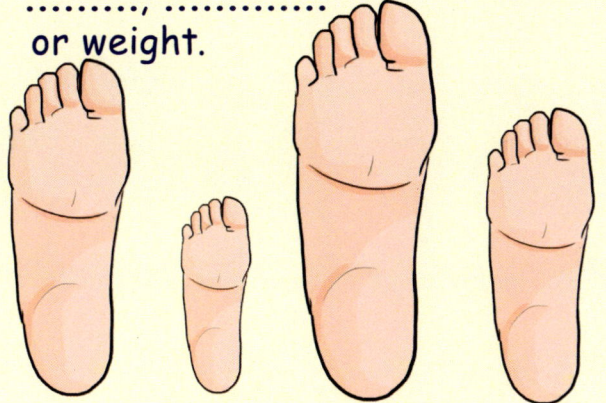

19 .... Variation and Environmental ....

- Environmental factors affect .... variation .... than discontinuous (.................) variations.

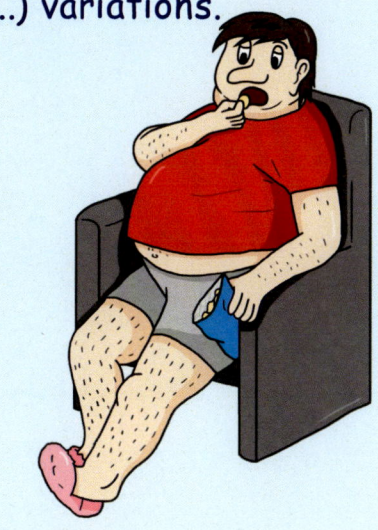

20   Collecting Continuous Data

- For .... **data** like height, weight and foot length, we can still use a .... **chart**.

- As data changes **gradually**, we need .... not just categories.

- The ranges we choose must be able to record .... the data.

Height	Number of People
Up to 130cm	卌
131-135cm	卌 卌
136-140cm	卌 卌 卌
141-145cm	卌 卌 卌 ||
146-150cm	卌 卌 卌
151-155cm	卌 卌
156-160cm	卌

21   Plotting .... Data

- We can then plot a graph from the data that we have collected.

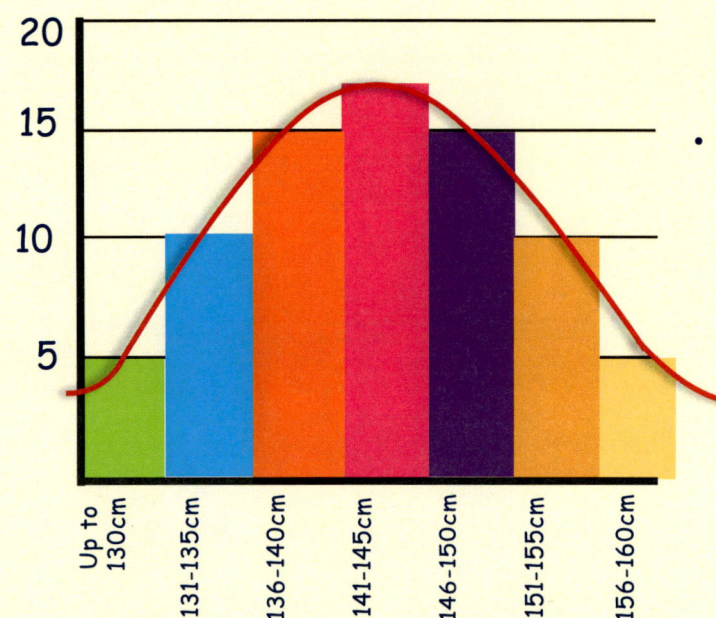

- A .... is used to plot .... **of** ...., for example how height changes in your form.

- If we draw a line that goes through the tops of all our columns, it makes a ....

22   'Bell' Shape = Continuous Variation

- .... **variation** graphs **always** give us a ...... **shape**.

- Sometimes the .... may be taller, or shorter, sometimes it may be pushed to one side, but it will always be there!

23   Correlations

- If there is a .... between two or more sets of data, we say that there is a ....

- There is a .... between the .... you walk and the .... it takes you.

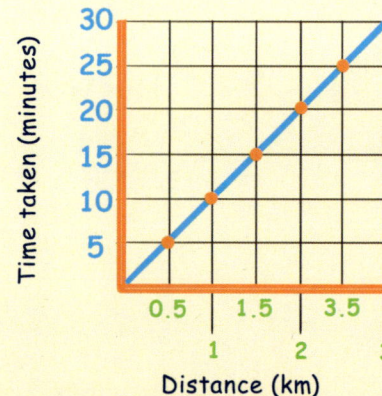

Words to help you...

backbone   selective breeding   teeth   genes   cows
genetic modification   breeding   species   questions   milk
birth   produce   examples   GM

24   Why Are Correlations Important?

Correlations help answer ....

- For example: if farmers feed their .... more, how much more .... will they ....?

25   Making Changes

- .... is when only certain .... of a species are used for ....

- .... (....) is the **variation of** .... to make a certain **characteristic**.

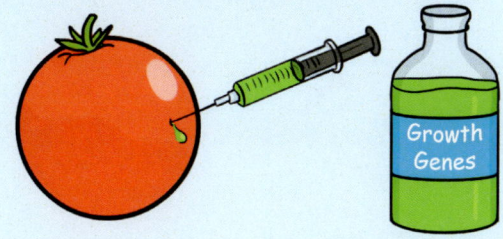

Growth Genes

- Think about the good **and** the bad effects of these.

26   Looking At Features

- Lots of .... look different but have a lot in common.

- A hippopotamus and a sheep look different but...

- They both have eyes and ears.

- They both have .... for eating plants.

- They both give .... to live young.

- They both have a ....

Words to help you...

animal   5   mammals   vertebrates   reptiles   classification
plant   groups   amphibians   features   fungi   fish
Kingdoms   bacteria   protists   birds

27 Classification

- We can use common .... to put **organisms** into ....

- We call this ....

- There are ... major ....:

  - ....
  - P............
  - ....
  - ....
  - P............

28 The Animal Kingdom

- In the **Animal Kingdom** there are 5 groups of ....:

1. Mammals

2. B.......

3. R........

4. A..........

5. F......

29 Animals

- .... include humans, monkeys, bats and dolphins.

- .... include blackbirds, robins and eagles.

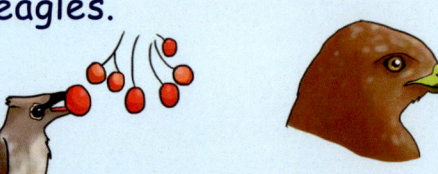

- .... include lizards, crocodiles and snakes.

30 Animals

- .... include frogs, toads and newts.

- .... include goldfish, salmon and cod.

- Each group has common ....

31   M..........

All ....…

- have body .... or fur.

- give birth to .... young.

- produce ....

- are .... blooded.

- have a backbone (they are ....).

32   B......

All ....…

- have feathers and ....

- lay ..... with hard shells.

- breathe with ....

- are .... blooded.

- have a .... (**vertebrates**).

33   R.........

All ....…

- have dry, ... skin.

- lay .... with shells.

- breathe with ....

- are ...... blooded.

- have a backbone (..................).

34   A.............

All **amphibians**...

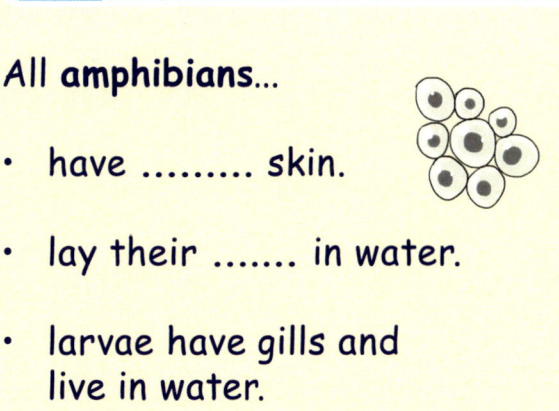

- have .... skin.

- lay their .... in water.

- larvae have gills and live in water.

- adults have lungs and live on .... and in ....

- are ...... blooded.

- have a .... (**vertebrates**).

35   F......

All ....

- live in ....
- breathe with ....
- have .... bodies.
- have bony ....
- are .... blooded.
- have a back bone (..................).

36   **Vertebrates and Invertebrates**

Animals are mainly broken into two groups:

- ....
  (Animals with a backbone)

- ....
  (Animals without a backbone)

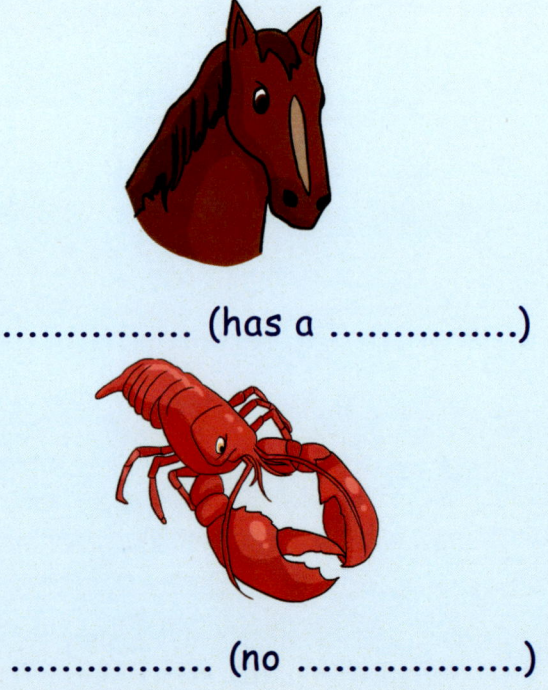

.... (has a ....)

.... (no ....)

37   Invertebrates

Most **invertebrates** have...

- a ...... outer coating on the body (...............).

- .... and a ....

38   Invertebrate Variations

- **Invertebrates** do .... have a backbone.

- ......, insects, crustaceans,....... and worms are all ....

- .... (echinoderms) are also invertebrates!

39   A.........

- Spiders and ticks are ....

- They have ... legs.

- Body is in ... parts.

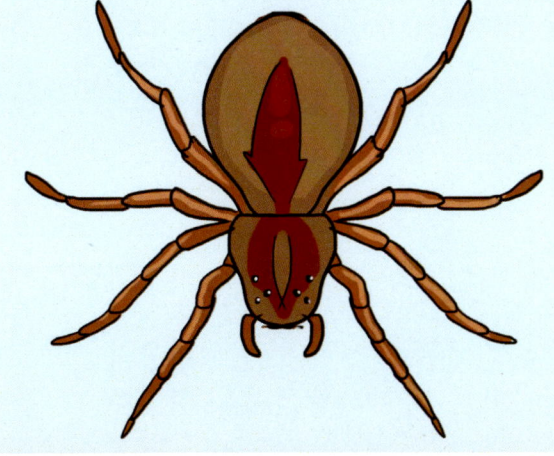

40   Insects

- They have ... legs.

- ... body parts (......, thorax, abdomen).

- ... antennae.

- May have up to ... pairs of wings.

Words to help you...

body underground groups organisms kingdoms snails
sea species legs woodlice one classify worms
slugs animals oysters foot

41 Crustaceans

- **Crustaceans** have different numbers of .....

- Many live in the .....

- Others, like ...., live on the land.

42 W.......

- .... have long, tube-like bodies.

- They can be found living in many different places - ...., under the .... or inside other ....!

43 Molluscs

- Have a head, body and foot all as ..... part.

- This group includes ...., ... and many sea organisms like mussels and ....

Eye

....

....

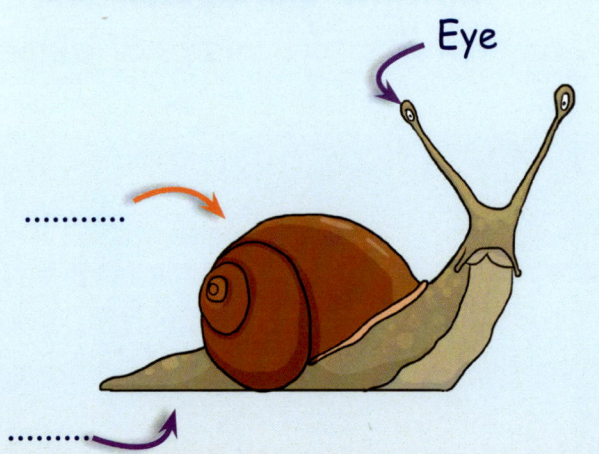

44 Sorting Species

- There are millions of .... on our planet.

- Many .... have similar features.

- We use these features to .... them into their .... , **classes** and ....

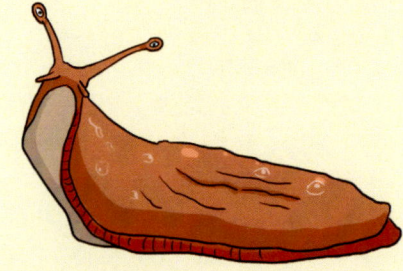

45   Recap on Kingdoms

We can sort **organisms** into 5 major kingdoms.

1.   ....

2.   ....

3.   ....

4.   ....

5.   .... (anything that is

    not a plant, animal or fungus).

46   Classification

Each **kingdom** is **subdivided** into smaller **groups**.

We have looked at 7 **groups** so far...
1.   M.............
2.   R.............
3.   A.............
4.   B......
5.   F.......
6.   V.................
7.   I.................

Now, let's see where they all fit in.

47   The Five Kingdoms

F........   Plants   ....   Bacteria   P...........

The **Animal Kingdom** is split into two:
.... (with a backbone) and
.... (no backbone).

Vertebrates

Invertebrates

Vertebrates are split into 5 groups.

Invertebrates can be divided into s............, i..............., crustaceans, m............. and w...........

48   T............ Classification

- T.................... Classification is the **scientific** .... for identifying, naming and classifying ....

- The same .... for .... are used all over the world.

49   Keys

- We use .... to identify, and put, ... into their correct ....

- A **key** is a set of questions needing a "......" or "...." answer.

For example...

- Does the **animal** have dry, scaly skin?

- Does the **animal** live in water?

Invertebrate Key

Start Here → Has it got legs?

Has it got legs?
- YES → Has it got 6 legs?
- NO → Has its body got several parts (segments)?

Has it got 6 legs?
- YES → ....

Has it got 8 legs? (NO from 6 legs)
- YES → Does its body only have 1 part?
- NO → Has it got an oval shaped body?

Does its body only have 1 part?
- YES → Harvestman
- NO → ....

Has it got an oval shaped body?
- YES → ....
- NO → Has it got one pair of legs for each segment of its body?

Has it got one pair of legs for each segment of its body?
- YES → ....
- NO → ....

Has its body got several parts (segments)?
- YES → ....
- NO → Has it got a shell?

Has it got a shell?
- YES → ....
- NO → ....

About Oaka Books

Children learn best when they are engaged...

Our aim is to help children enjoy learning by making it fun! That way they will succeed.

Following Common Entrance and National Curriculum guidelines for KS3.

Design and layout of our books follow guidelines from the British Dyslexia Association

Three Easy Steps

Read: the easy to follow bullet point Topic Booklet.

Engage: Play the Active Learning Game.

Learn: When you understand the topic, test yourself using the Write Your Own Notes Book. You can use the Topic Booklet to help if you get stuck.

One (short) Topic at a time:

For some students, a big book is a big turn off. That's why we focus on one topic at a time. Short and to the point.

Reading Age

This booklet is suitable for children with a reading age of 10 ½ years.

Topic Packs for KS1, KS2 & KS3 Include:

History
Geography
Chemistry
Biology
Physics

Please visit www.oakabooks.co.uk for more information about forthcoming titles

© Copyright 2018 Oaka Books. All rights reserved.
Written by Stuart Lawes BSc PGCE. Illustrations by Joy Gardiner & Laurence Andrew Page.

First paperback edition printed 2015 in the United Kingdom.
A catalogue record for this book is available from the British Library.

ISBN 978-1-909892-53-8
No part of this book shall be reproduced or transmitted in any form or by any means, electronic or mechanical, including photocopying, recording or by any information retrieval system without written permission of the copyright owner or a licence permitting restricted copying issued by the Copyright Licensing Agency Ltd, Saffron House, 6-10 Kirby Street, London EC1N 8TS Tel: 020 7400 3100   Fax: 020 7400 3101   Email: cla@cla.co.uk   Web: www.cla.co.uk

Designed, set and published by Oaka™ Books.

To order other titles from Oaka™ Books, please email info@oakabooks.co.uk or visit www.oakabooks.co.uk, or phone: +44 (0) 2392 388519.

Acknowledgements
Our huge thanks go to the many teachers who have been involved in the development of this series of learning guides. Special thanks to Joy Gardiner, for producing hundreds of illustrations, to Kate Doehren, for her enthusiasm and invaluable assistance to my wonderful daughter Sophie, for being the inspiration for the books and, of course, to Charlie, for believing in them.

ISBN 978-1-911189-56-5

CE/KS3
Variation & Classifica-
Write Your Own Notes Booklet

ISBN 978-1-909892-53-8   Produced in association with Kate Doehren, MA Ed, B.Ed Hons, RSA Dip, Sp LD/Dyslexia
Head of Learning Support, Hurstpierpoint College
© Copyright Oaka™ Books 2018